Charlie, Charlie,
Chuck chuck chuck,
Went to bed
With two young ducks.
One died,
Charie cried,
Charlie Charlie,
Chuck chuck chuck.

Charlie Barley
Scittery legs,
Sold his mother
Two duck eggs,
One was rotten
Good for nothing,
Charlie Barley
Scittery legs.

3

Winnie the witch
Fell in a ditch
Found a penny
Thought she was rich.

She went to the bank man
The bank man said:
"It's only a penny
You can't be rich!"

Martin Martin
The cow is fartin'
Where? Where?
Under the chair
Quick quick
Get the gun
Oh my God!
It's already done!

Dan, Dan the funny wee man,
Washed his face in a frying pan
Combed his hair
With the leg of a chair
Dan, Dan the funny wee man.

5

John John the piper's son
Went to school with nothing on
Teacher teacher that's not fair
Give me back my underwear

Ellie Smellie
Slipped in jelly
Broke her belly
Watching telly!

Ouch!

The cow kicked Ellie in the belly in the barn
Ellie said the cow didn't do her any harm
She gave me a bottle and a bottle of the best
And she let me put my two arms
Right around her chest

What's the easiest biscuit to fly?

The plain one

Who did the skeleton dance with at the disco?

No-body!

Why did the skeleton get married ?
'Cos he had no-body.

Why can a car not play football?

Because it has only one boot.

Three young rats in satin suits
Three young cats in leather boots
Three young ducks in gabardines
Three young dogs in denim jeans
Went out to walk with two young pigs
In mini-skirts and orange wigs
But suddenly it changed to rain
And so they all went back again

Ellie Ward heard this from her father who heard it from his aunt.

10

There was an old man from Leeds
He swallowed a packet of seeds
No longer than an hour
His face was a flower
And his hands were a bunch of weeds

Sasha McDonagh heard this from his father, who heard it from his father.

There was a young man called Joe
He dreamed he ate his toe
He fell out of bed
and he bounced his head
And he went for a roll in the snow

Loorabug Larabug Lincoln Lock
Five miles to seven o'clock
We sat, we sang, we daily sprang
When out came Nod with his long rod
And chased us all from wink to wall
Right down pickety packety pie

One fine day in the middle of the night
Two dead men got up to fight
Too blind were watching on
Too deaf and dumb said hurry on
Too crippled ran for the guards

An old lady and an old man were going to Dublin on the bus. The old man had a pipe in his mouth and the old lady had a dog on her lap.

The old lady took the pipe and pegged it out the window. The old man pegged the dog out the door. They went on a mile anyways and came back.

What do you think the dog had in his mouth?

His tongue

15

The artwork for this book was created by a variety of art techniques.

Printing: We made simple card prints by drawing onto soft card, then scoring with a variety of sharp implements to create texture and detail. An ordinary biro is the easiest to use in the classroom – simply press hard into the card. A print is taken by rolling printing ink lightly across the surface, before laying a clean sheet of paper on top, and rolling across this with a clean roller. Peel the paper away and hey presto you have a print. Several prints may be taken from the same inking, getting progressively lighter.

Charcoal drawing: We experimented with different styles of mark-making including line drawing, smudging, rubbing, and drawing back into charcoal with erasers.

Colour pastels: We experimented laying different colours over the black and white images using sheets of acetate

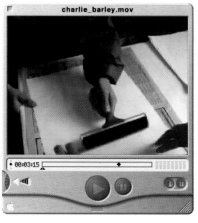

Making books: We made classroom books from photocopies of the prints and the texts to help design the final layout.

A set of posters is available to accompany the book from Kids' Own at admin@kidsown.ie

www.kidsown.ie